Karl Jenkins

GLORIA

for solo voice, chorus & orchestra

T0078678

Vocal score

BOOSEY & HAWKES

Boosey & Hawkes Music Publishers Ltd
www.boosey.com

Published by Boosey & Hawkes Music Publishers Ltd
Aldwych House
71–91 Aldwych
London
WC2B 4HN

www.boosey.com

ISMN 979-0-060-12083-1
ISBN 978-0-85162-598-0

First published 2010. Second edition 2010, with revisions. Sixth impression 2017, corrected.
This impression 2024

Printed by Halstan:
Halstan UK, 2–10 Plantation Road, Amersham, Bucks, HP6 6HJ. United Kingdom
Halstan DE, Weißliliengasse 4, 55116 Mainz. Germany

Cover design by RF Design UK Limited
Cover photo: Vasily Smirnov/istock
Music origination by Robin Hagues

CONTENTS

GLORIA

★See pages vi–viii for the text of readings

COMPOSER'S NOTE

The Latin text of the *Gloria* is an ancient hymn of praise from the Christian tradition derived from the song of the angels who announce the birth of Jesus, as recorded in the Gospel according to St Luke. The *Gloria* has formed part of the Ordinary of the Mass for many centuries, and in that context has been set by many composers; there are also independent settings by Handel, Vivaldi and Poulenc. But the opportunity to work with such an iconic text also afforded me an opportunity to explore how other religions perceive the Divine. This is an ongoing feature of my work, from the multi-faceted *The Armed Man: A Mass for Peace*, the Japanese haiku in my *Requiem* to the ancient Arabic text in my *Stabat Mater*.

My setting of the *Gloria* uses the Latin text in the first, second and fifth movements, 'The Proclamation', 'The Prayer' and 'The Exaltation'. Other, related Biblical texts appear in the middle movements. The third is called 'The Psalm' and sets Psalm 150, a psalm of praise sung in Hebrew (though it may alternatively be performed in Latin). The fourth movement, 'The Song', is my own English adaptation of verses from Deuteronomy, Psalm 144 and the First Book of Chronicles.

Between these movements are readings I have chosen from the texts of other ancient religions, performed in chronological order of their establishment. The texts focus on each religion's concept of the divine or the Ultimate Reality, eternal and unchanging. This concept is a unifying feature of all world religions, commonly defined as a personal and loving God or as an eternal truth that governs the universe.

> Hinduism: an excerpt from the *Bhagavadgītā* (Song of the Divine), the classic Hindu scripture

> Buddhism: the last lines of the *Diamond Sūtra*, the world's oldest dated printed book

> Taoism: the opening of the principal Taoist scripture, the *Tao Te Ching* (The Classic of the Way and Virtue)

> Islam: the first chapter of the *Qur'an*, known as 'Al Fatiha' (The Opening), which is recited in Muslim daily prayers

The *Gloria* is scored for choir and orchestra with the addition, common to my work, of ethnic percussion instruments, indigenous to those cultures mentioned above.

Karl Jenkins
June 2010

I. The Proclamation: Gloria in excelsis Deo

Gloria in excelsis Deo.
Et in terra pax hominibus bonæ voluntatis.

Glory to God in the highest,
and on earth peace to men of good will.

Reading from the Hindu *Bhagavadgītā*
(The Song of the Divine) (Sanskrit)

aham ātmā guḍākeśa sarvabhūtaśayasthitaḥ,
aham ādiś ca madhyaṃ ca
   bhūtānām anta eva ca.

Bhagavadgītā 10: 20

I am the Self, O Arjuna, dwelling in the hearts
of all beings. I am the beginning, the middle,
and the end of all beings.

brahmaṇo hi
   pratiṣṭhāham amṛtasyāvyayasya ca,
śāśvatasya ca dharmasya
   sukhasyaikāntikasya ca.

Bhagavadgītā 14: 27

I am the glory of Brahman, the immortal
and immutable, of Eternal Dharma, and of
Absolute Bliss.

English translation: Ushma Sheth

II. The Prayer: Laudamus te

Laudamus te.
Benedicimus te.
Adoramus te.
Glorificamus te.
Gratias agimus tibi
   propter magnam gloriam tuam.

We praise you.
We bless you.
We adore you.
We glorify you.
We give thanks to you for your great glory.

Reading from the Buddhist *Diamond Sūtra* (Buddhist Hybrid Sanskrit)

tārakātimiraṃ dīpo māyāvaśyāyā
   budbudam,
supinaṃ vidyud abhraṃ ca evaṃ draṣṭavyā
   saṃskṛtam.

Verse inserted before stanza 32 of the Diamond
Sūtra *(Sanskrit title:* Vajracchedikā-
prajñāpāramitā-sūtra*)*

Like a tiny drop of dew, or a bubble floating in
   a stream;
Like a flash of lightning in a summer cloud,
Or a flickering lamp, an illusion, a phantom,
   or a dream.
So is all conditioned existence to be seen.

English translation: Alex Johnson

III. The Psalm: Tehillim – Psalm 150

Hal(e)lu-Yah, hal(e)lu-El b(e)kodsho.
Hal(e)luhu bir(e)kia uzo.

Hal(e)luhu big(e)vurotav.
Hal(e)luhu kh(e)rov gud(e)lo.

Hal(e)luhu b(e)teka shofar.
Hal(e)luhu b(e)nevel v(e)khinor.

Hal(e)luhu b(e)tof umakhol.
Hal(e)luhu b(e)minim v(e)ugav.

Hal(e)luhu b(e)tsilts(e)ley shama.
Hal(e)luhu b(e)tsilts(e)ley t(e)rua.
Kol han(e)shama t(e)halel Yah.

Hal(e)lu-Yah!

Alternative Latin text:

Laudate Dominum in sanctis ejus.
Laudate eum in firmamento virtutis ejus.

Laudate eum in virtutibus ejus.
Laudate eum secundum multitudinem
    magnitudinis ejus.

Laudate eum in sono tubæ.
Laudate eum in psalterio et cithara.

Laudate eum in tympano et choro.
Laudate eum in chordis et organo.

Laudate eum in cymbalis benesonantibus.
Laudate eum in cymbalis jubilationis.
Omnis spiritus laudet Dominum.

Alleluia!

O praise God in his holiness.
Praise him in the firmament of his power.

Praise him for his noble acts.
Praise him according to his excellent
    greatness.

Praise him in the sound of the trumpet.
Praise him with the psaltery and harp.

Praise him with the timbrel and dance.
Praise him upon the strings and pipe.

Praise him upon the well-tuned cymbals.
Praise him upon the loud cymbals.
Let every thing that has breath praise the Lord.

Reading from the Taoist *Tao Te Ching*
(The Classic of the Way and Virtue) (Chinese)

Dao ke dao, fei chang dao
Ming ke ming, fei chang ming
Wu ming, tian di zhi shi
You ming, wan wu zhi mu

Gu chang wu, yu yi guan qi miao
Chang you, yu yi guan qi jiao

Ci liang zhe tong chu er yi ming
Tong wei zhi xuan
Xuan zhi you xuan
Zhong miao zhi men

The Way that words can tell is not the eternal Way.
The name that words can name is not the
    eternal name.
The nameless is the source of heaven and earth.
The named is the mother of myriad forms.

Free from desire: behold the unknowable.
Filled with desire: behold the visible.

Being and non-being springing from the source,
and differing only in their name:
this is the deepest mystery,
the darkness of the dark,
this is the gateway opening to the All.

English paraphase by Grahame Davies from
existing translations

IV. The Song: I'll make music

Lord and Master, I'll sing a song to you,
on the ten-string lyre I'll make music.
Lord and Master, let your thoughts fall like
    rain
and just like showers on new grass.

We'll play for you with harps and trumpets,
we'll sing some psalms in praise of you,
we'll play for you with flutes and cymbals,
we'll sing some psalms in praise of you.

Lord and Master, I'll sing a song to you,
on the ten-string lyre, I'll sing praises to you.
Lord and Master, let your words descend like
    dew
and just like droplets on tender leaves.

We'll play for you with harps and trumpets,
we'll sing some psalms in praise of you,
we'll play for you with flutes and cymbals,
we'll sing some psalms in praise of you.

I'll make music, I shall make new music,
I shall make music for you.

Deuteronomy 32: 2, Psalm 144: 9 and
1 Chronicles 13: 8, adapted by Karl Jenkins

Reading from the *Qur'an*: 'Al Fatiha'
(The Opening) (Arabic)

Bismillāhi r-raḥmāni r-raḥīm
Al ḥamdu lillāhi rabbi l-'ālamīn
Ar raḥmāni r-raḥīm
Māliki yawmi d-dīn
Iyyāka na'budu wa iyyāka nasta'īn

In the name of God, the Beneficent, the Merciful.
Praise be to God, Lord of the Worlds,
The Beneficent, the Merciful.
Master of the Day of Judgment,
Thee we worship, and Thy help we seek.

English translation by Marmaduke Pickthall,
from *The Meaning of the Glorious Quran*
(1938) (adapted)

V. The Exaltation: Domine Deus

Domine Deus, Rex cælestis,
Deus Pater omnipotens.
Domine Fili unigenite, Jesu Christe.
Domine Deus, Agnus Dei, Filius Patris.
Qui tollis peccata mundi, miserere nobis.

Qui tollis peccata mundi, suscipe
  deprecationem nostram.
Qui sedes ad dexteram Patris, miserere nobis.

Quoniam tu solus sanctus, tu solus Dominus,
  tu solus Altissimus, Jesu Christe, cum
  Sancto Spiritu, in gloria Dei Patris. Amen.

Lord God, heavenly King,
God the Father almighty.
Lord Jesus Christ, only-begotten Son.
Lord God, Lamb of God, Son of the Father.
You who takes away the sins of the world,
  have mercy on us.
You who takes away the sins of the world,
  hear our prayer.
You who sits at the right hand of the Father,
  have mercy on us.
For you alone are holy, you alone are the
  Lord, you alone are the Most High, Jesus
  Christ, with the Holy Spirit in the glory of
  God the Father. Amen.

PERFORMANCE NOTES

'The Psalm' may be sung in Hebrew or Latin.

'The Song' may be sung by any solo voice, either in the original key or a semitone higher. Orchestral parts include this movement in both keys.

The spoken texts may be read in English or any language of choice.

The orchestration mirrors that of the standard (larger) scoring of Fauré's *Requiem*, with the addition of percussion. There are optional extra wind parts.

HEBREW PRONUNCIATION GUIDE

All vowels (and diphthongs) are as in Italian.

(e) represents the 'shwa' [ə] or neutral vowel rather like the mute *e* in French. Where this letter does not have syllabic value, it has been omitted from the musical text.

All consonants as in English except:

kh = guttural *ch* as in Scottish *loch*
r should be rolled
sh is as in *ship*

ACKNOWLEDGMENTS

The composer and the publishers gratefully acknowledge the assistance of Mr Arfon Jones, and of Rabbi Donna Kirshbaum, Congregation String of Pearls, Princeton, New Jersey, in the preparation of the Hebrew text in the score. Also Grahame Davies for his invaluable help in researching ethnic texts and for paraphrasing in English the *Tao* extract, to Professor Clifford Wright for his advice regarding the *Diamond Sūtra*, to Ushma Sheth for translating the *Bhagavadgītā* passage, and to Leila Buheiry for her assistance with the *Qu'ran* translation.

Commissioned for Don Monro, founder of
Concerts from Scratch and The Really Big Chorus

First performed by The Really Big Chorus
and the London Festival Orchestra, conducted by Brian Kay,
at the Royal Albert Hall, London, on 11 July 2010

First recording: EMI CD 50999 6 46430 2 1,
by the National Youth Choir of Great Britain (director: Mike Brewer),
Jody K Jenkins (ethnic percussion) and the
London Symphony Orchestra, conducted by Karl Jenkins

INSTRUMENTATION

2 Flutes (2nd doubling Piccolo)
2 Oboes (optional)
2 Clarinets in B♭ (2nd doubling Bass Clarinet)
2 Bassoons (2nd optionally doubling Contrabassoon)
4 Horns in F
2 or 3 Trumpets in B♭
3 Trombones
Tuba (optional)
Timpani
Percussion (3)★
Harp
Organ (optional)
Strings

★ 1: side drum, surdo, finger cymbals, cymbals

2: triangle, cabasa, tambourine (or goblet drum *etc*),
hand drum (darbuca, congas *etc*), cymbals, suspended cymbal

3: glockenspiel, xylophone, bass drum

Note. One triangle and one pair of cymbals are required in total

Duration: 34 minutes

Performance materials available on hire

GLORIA

KARL JENKINS
(b 1944)

I. The Proclamation:
Gloria in excelsis Deo

19070

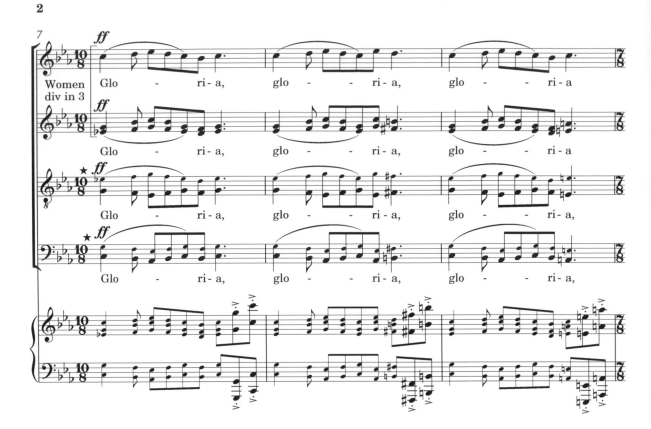

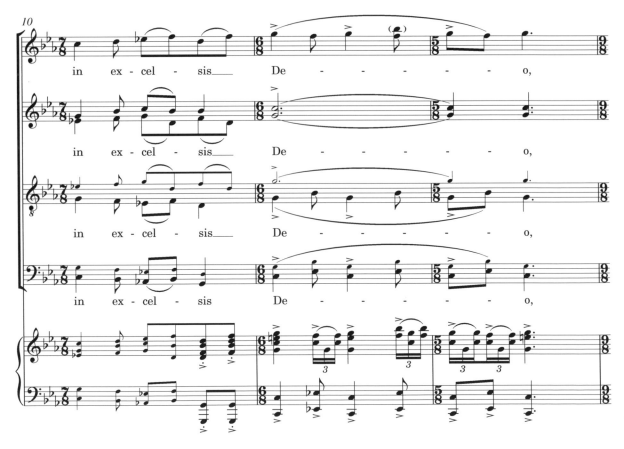

4

De - o, in ex-cel -sis___ De -

De - o, in ex-cel -sis___ De -

De - o, in ex-cel - sis De -

De - o, in ex-cel - sis De -

rall GP

- - - - - - - - - o.

- - - o.

- - - - - - - - - - o.

- - - - - - - - - - o.

rall GP

★ small notes indicate optional divisi

19070

in ex - cel - sis___ De - - - - - o,
in ex - cel - sis___ De - - - - - o,
in ex - cel - sis___ De - - - - - o,
in ex - cel - sis De - - - - - o,

De - o, De - o, in ex - cel - sis___
De - o, De - o, in ex - cel - sis___
De - o, De - o, in ex - cel - sis___
De - o, De - o, in ex - cel - sis

II. The Prayer: Laudamus te

★ Close immediately on to the 'm' of 'tuam' to begin seamless humming in all parts to letter I

19070

III. The Psalm: Tehillim – Psalm 150

Giubiloso ♩. = 130–135

19070

11 optional hand claps

★ Either the Latin or the Hebrew text is to be sung, at conductor's discretion

19070

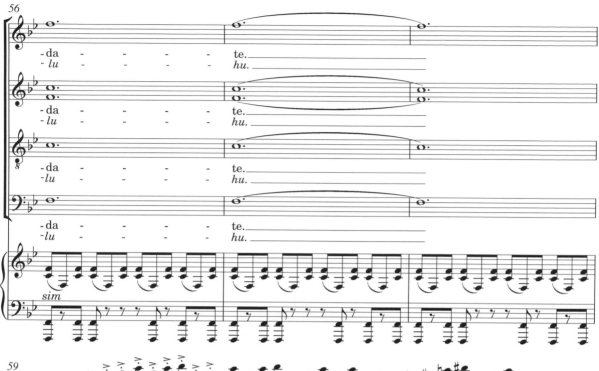

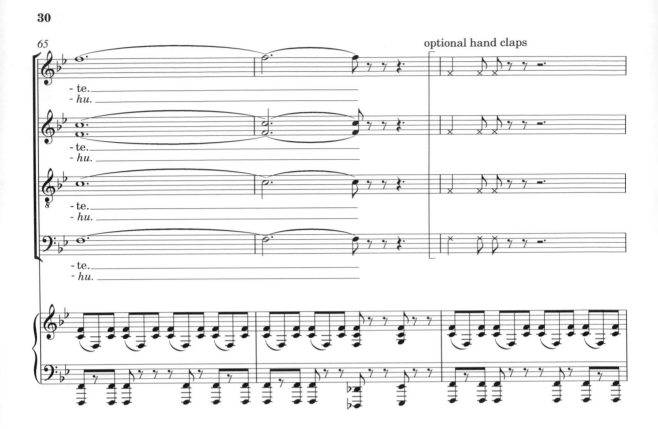

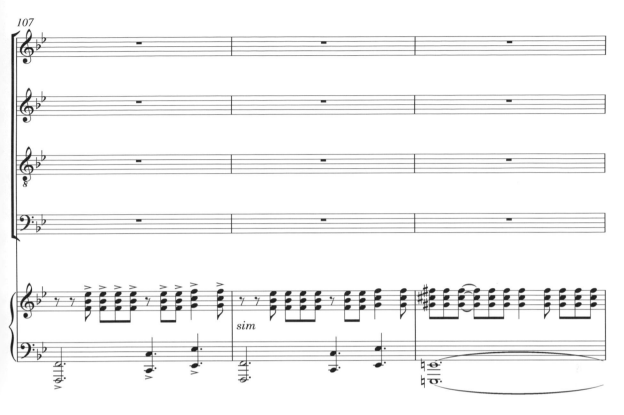

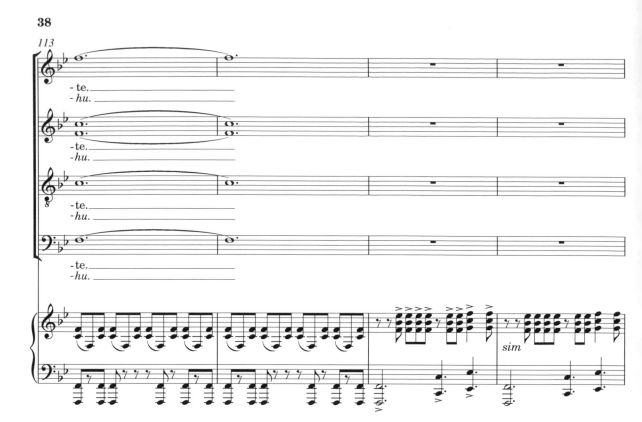

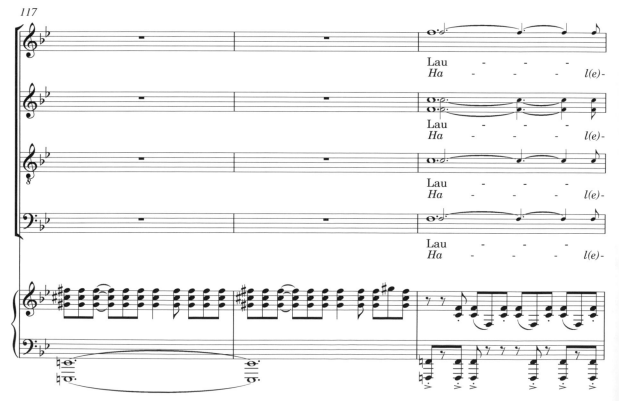

IV. The Song: I'll make music

Deuteronomy 32: 2, Psalm 144: 9
& 1 Chronicles 13: 8,
adapted by Karl Jenkins

★This movement may be sung by any suitable voice, male or female, and it may be sung a semitone higher if required. Orchestral materials are provided in both keys.

Lord___ and Mas - ter, let your thoughts fall like rain and___ just like show-ers

on___ new grass, new grass, show-ers on new grass.

P **Un poco più mosso**

We'll play for you with harps and trumpets,

we'll sing some psalms in praise of you,___ we'll play for you with flutes and

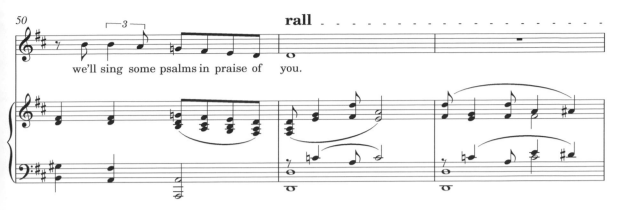

we'll sing some psalms in praise of you.

Tempo primo ♩ = 38–40

I'll make mu-sic, I shall make new_ mu-sic,

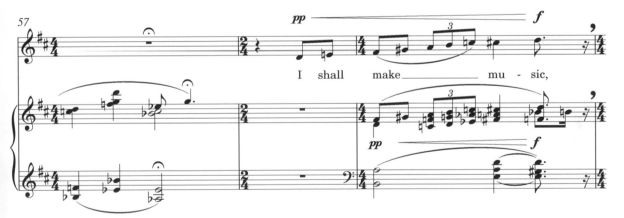

I shall make_____ mu - sic,

mu-sic for you._____

V. The Exaltation: Domine Deus

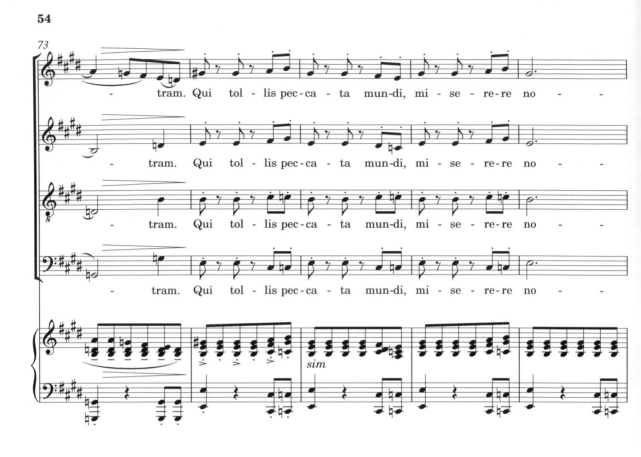

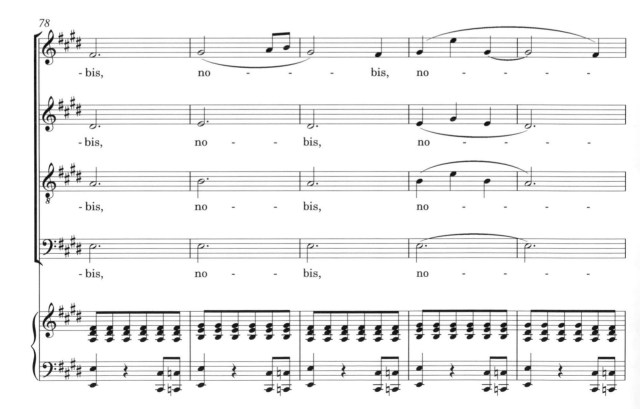

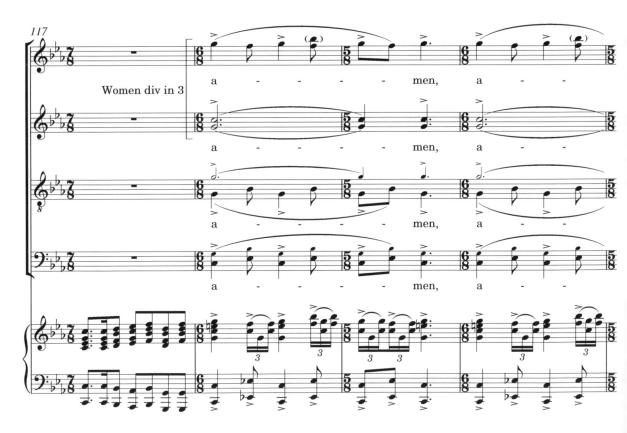

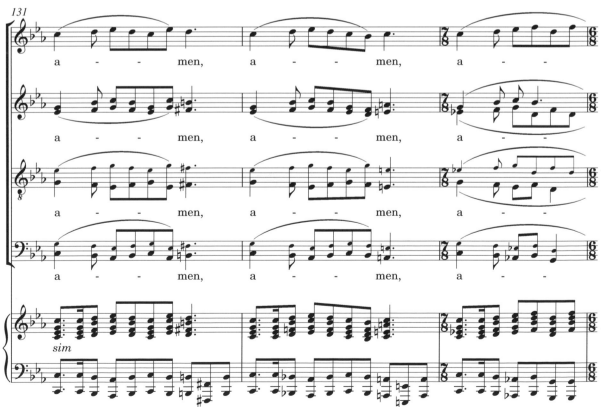

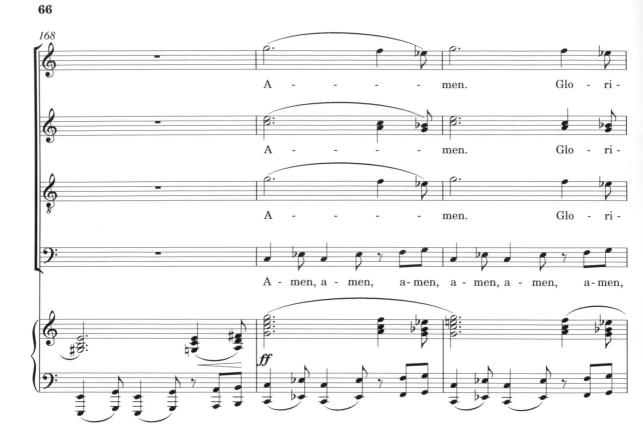